If you have
and been s
bother
then you will understand...

Text by Lois Rock
Text copyright © 1996 Lion Publishing
Illustrations copyright © 1996 Roger Langton

Published by
Lion Publishing plc
Sandy Lane West, Littlemore, Oxford, England
ISBN 0 7459 3110 3
Albatross Books Pty Ltd
PO Box 320, Sutherland, NSW 2232, Australia
ISBN 0 7324 0970 5

First edition 1996
10 9 8 7 6 5 4 3 2 1 0

A catalogue record for this book
is available from the British Library

Printed and bound in Singapore

**This retelling is based on the stories
of Jesus' life in the Bible.**

Jesus' Story
of the
Kind Enemy

Retold by Lois Rock
Illustrations by Roger Langton

A LION BOOK

Jesus spent a lot of time telling people about God and listening to their questions.

Some people tried to ask him the hardest questions they could think of. They hoped Jesus would give a wrong answer and end up looking silly.

"What must I do so that I can live as God's friend for ever?" asked one man.

His job was to teach people about God, so he thought he knew the right answer.

"You've read the books with God's laws in," said Jesus. "What do they say?"

The man answered: "First of all, love God. Next, love other people. Be as kind to them as you are to yourself."

"Quite right," said Jesus. "You knew already."

"But which other people do I need to love?" asked the man. So Jesus told this story.

"One day, a man was going down the road from Jerusalem to Jericho. Robbers attacked him and took all he had.

"They beat him up and left him lying
hurt in the road.

"A priest came by—a priest from the temple in Jerusalem. He helped people follow God's laws.

"But when he saw the man lying in the road, he pretended not to see and hurried by.

"A Levite came by—a helper in the same temple where people came to worship God.

"He saw the man and came closer to look. Then he hurried away too.

"A Samaritan was also travelling along that road."

Now, people from Jerusalem didn't like Samaritans. Samaritans didn't worship God in the right way and they didn't have a proper temple. Samaritans were enemies to the people listening to Jesus' story.

"The Samaritan saw the man, and he wanted to help. So he bandaged up the man's wounds. He helped the man on to his own donkey and took him to an inn.

" 'Please look after this man for me,'
he asked the innkeeper. 'Here are
coins to pay for what you do. If it costs
more, I'll pay you on my way back.'

"That's the story," said Jesus. "Here's a question. Who do you think showed love to the person who got hurt?"

"The one who was kind to him," said the man.

"Quite right," said Jesus. "Now you go and do the same."

A Christian prayer

Dear God,
Because you love us
we can love you
and we can love ourselves.
Your kindness and love
help us learn how to love others:
to be gentle with our friends,
to be kind to our enemies.
Amen.